Editor
Lorin Klistoff, M.A.

Managing Editor
Karen Goldfluss, M.S. Ed.

Illustrator
Kelly McMahon

Cover Artist
Brenda DiAntonis

Art Manager
Kevin Barnes

Art Director
CJae Froshay

Imaging
Alfred Lau

Publisher
Mary D. Smith, M.S. Ed.

MATH IN ACTION

Activities & Games for 0–10

Grades Pre·K-K

· Hands-on activities · Easy-to-use manipulatives · Lessons & objectives included

Author

Bev Dunbar

(Revised and rewritten by Teacher Created Resources, Inc.)

This edition published by *Teacher Created Resources, Inc.*
6421 Industry Way
Westminster, CA 92683
www.teachercreated.com

ISBN-1-4206-3529-8

©*2005 Teacher Created Resources, Inc.*

Made in U.S.A.
with permission by Blake Education

Table of Contents

#3529 Math in Action   ©Teacher Created Resources, Inc.

Introduction

Here are ten easy-to-use, multi-purpose activities and games to help make early number learning come alive in your classroom. This is a companion book to TCR 3524 *Math in Action: Number Activities 0–10*.

The ten themes have immediate appeal for young students, who will love manipulating frogs, dogbones, and freckles as part of their daily math activities. And with ten activities, there is plenty for up to a whole class to use together, working in groups of three or more.

Each activity has been designed to help your students practice recognizing, matching, and using numbers 0–10 in an imaginative way, with follow-up ideas for using the numbers 11–19. To help you with your planning, there is a set of skills matched to each activity.

There are also mini-posters showing how children count 0–10 in eight other languages (See pages 89–96). Encourage students who speak another language to share their number names with the whole class. Make your own posters for counting 0–10 in other languages to place beside the ones provided in this book.

All you need to get started is a small group of parent helpers to photocopy, color, laminate, and cut out for you, following the handy step-by-step instructions included with each activity.

You will also need an inexpensive storage container for each activity. Sample labels for each container have been included at the back of this book (See pages 82 and 83.). The best containers are those with clear sides and colorful, easy-to-put-on lids! Enlarge or reduce the labels to fit your containers.

With your enthusiastic students and some brief explanations from you, you are ready to go! You will have fun using these games and activities in your classroom.

Catering for Different Abilities

Each game or activity can be adapted to suit the needs of at least three ability groups within your class. After introducing the materials (See the start of each teacher's page for ideas.), allow time for free exploration. Then explain one of the activities shown on the teacher's cards or from the summary below. The teacher cards include a dot code to indicate the three levels.

Level One = ●
Level Two = ● ●
Level Three = ● ● ●

These cards can also be used by parent helpers in your classroom.

Level One

Matching

❏ Have students work in groups of three or more. Have each student select one small numeral or number word card and put the number of objects shown onto his or her large card.

❏ Have students make up a story to match their actions. (e.g., "This man had a fright. All his hair fell out except for these 6 hairs!")

Other Group Ideas

❏ Have each student place objects onto a large card and find the small card to match. Have him or her turn this face down, or cover it up. Have him or her ask a partner to guess the number on the small card.

❏ Have each student place some objects onto a large card. Have him or her guess how many objects there are altogether and then check by counting. Have him or her find a small card to match.

❏ Have students roll a 1–6 dot/numeral die or spin a 0–9 spinner, then collect the matching number of objects. Have them find out who has the most after each round.

❏ Use the eight sample language posters that show numbers 0–10 to identify number cards and count objects in each language.

❏ For extension groups, have students spin the 10–19 spinner or choose a 10–19 card and place the matching number of objects onto a large card.

Level Two

Ordering and Making Patterns

❏ In groups, pairs, or individually, have students practice sorting the cards forward and backward into counting order.

❏ Have students find cards with the same/more/fewer objects than a given set.

❏ Have students make a pattern using the objects in the set. Have each student ask a partner to predict the next few items in the pattern.

#3529 Math in Action

Catering for Different Abilities

Level Two

Other Group Ideas

- ❑ Have students mix up objects or counters between two or more sets. Have each student invent an interesting pattern and challenge a partner to identify, then continue, the pattern.

- ❑ Have each student place up to 19 objects onto a large card. Have him or her guess how many objects altogether, then check by counting.

- ❑ Have each student put three or more cards from 0–19 into counting order forward or backward.

- ❑ Have students roll the 7–12 die or spin the 10–19 spinner, then collect the matching number of objects. Ask, "Who has the most after each round? The fewest? The same number?"

Level Three

Operations

- ❑ Have students identify how many objects they start with and then add or remove objects to match a new number.

- ❑ Have each student take a handful of objects. Ask, "Can you share them equally amongst all the large cards?" Have students guess first, then check.

Other Group Ideas

- ❑ Have students identify whether there is an odd or an even number of objects. Have them explain how they know this.

- ❑ Have students make up a problem to match the theme. (e.g., "I'd like to have three more fish than you have. How many more fish do I need to put in my fish bowl?")

- ❑ Have each student take a small card and place a matching number of objects to a large card. Have him or her take another small card and place a matching number of objects onto the same card. Have him or her guess how many altogether, then check. Have him or her find a card to match this new number.

- ❑ Have each student match objects to a card, then challenge a partner to see how many equal groups they can make. (e.g., "Can you make groups of three?")

- ❑ Have each student spin the 10–19 spinner and collect the matching number of objects. Have each student spin the 0–9 spinner and remove the matching number of objects. Ask, "Who has the most after each round? The fewest? The same number?"

- ❑ Have students make up a game using the cards. (e.g., Throw two dice and take that many objects. Try to be the first to get exactly 20 objects on your large card.)

Feed the Monkeys

Introducing the Activity

❑ Discuss the way monkeys like to eat bananas.

❑ Have students pretend they are the zoo keepers. Tell them that each monkey likes to eat a specific number of bananas each day.

Skills

❑ Compares and orders sets of objects using one-to-one correspondence

❑ Represents numerals using objects or drawings

❑ Counts collections up to nine

❑ Identifies more or less than a given number

❑ Demonstrates understanding of simple addition

❑ Counts on mentally to add small numbers

How to Make the Game

❑ Make one copy of all the monkeys numbered 1–10 (pages 9–13) so that you have 10 monkeys.

❑ Color each one, laminate, and cut into individual monkeys.

❑ Make four copies of the bananas (page 14) onto yellow paper, or copy and color the bananas. Laminate and then cut out each banana.

❑ Copy, laminate, and cut out the four activity cards (pages 7 and 8).

❑ Place all the equipment into a storage container and label clearly. Use the label provided on page 82.

Extra Materials Needed

None

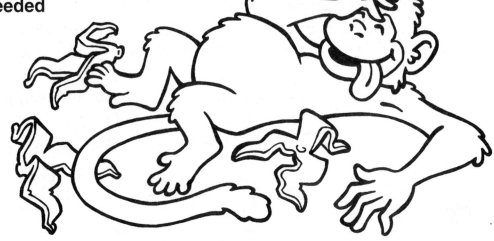

Feed a Monkey

✓ Pick a monkey. Look at the number.

✓ Feed the monkey the matching number of bananas.

✓ How many bananas are small?

  or
ONE   GROUP

Feed All the Monkeys

✓ Feed all the monkeys the matching number of bananas.
   Then turn each monkey over.

✓ Guess the monkey's number by looking at the bananas.

✓ Can you put the monkeys into counting order?

GROUP

7

Feed Two Monkeys

● ● ● ●

✓ Take two monkeys. Feed each monkey the matching number of bananas.

✓ How many bananas altogether?

✓ Guess first, and then check.

  or
ONE   PAIR

Bigger and Smaller

● ● ●

✓ Turn all the monkeys face down. Pick two monkeys. Which number is bigger?

✓ Pick one monkey. What is the next number?

✓ What is the number before?

✓ How do you know?

PAIR

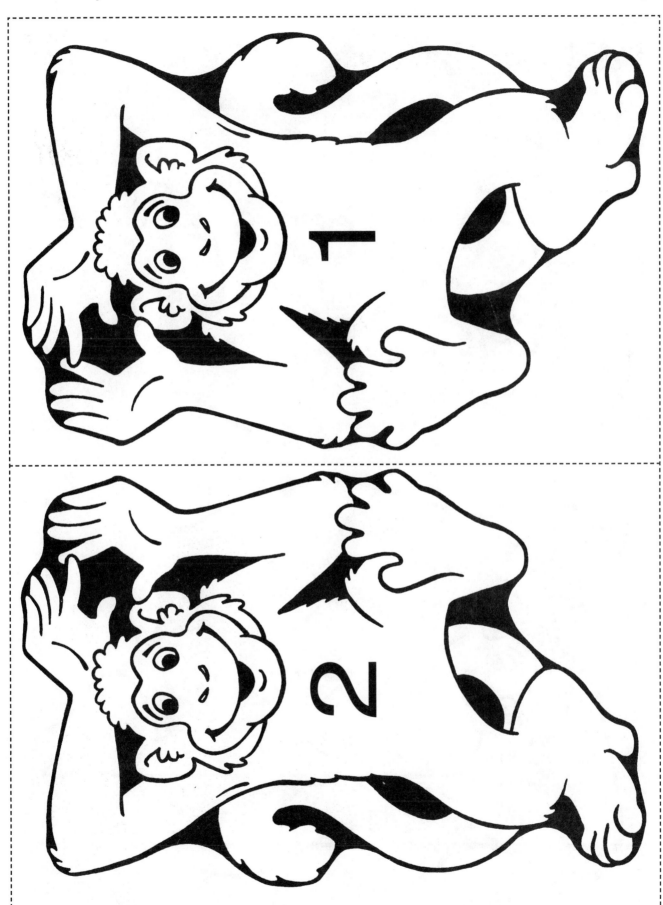

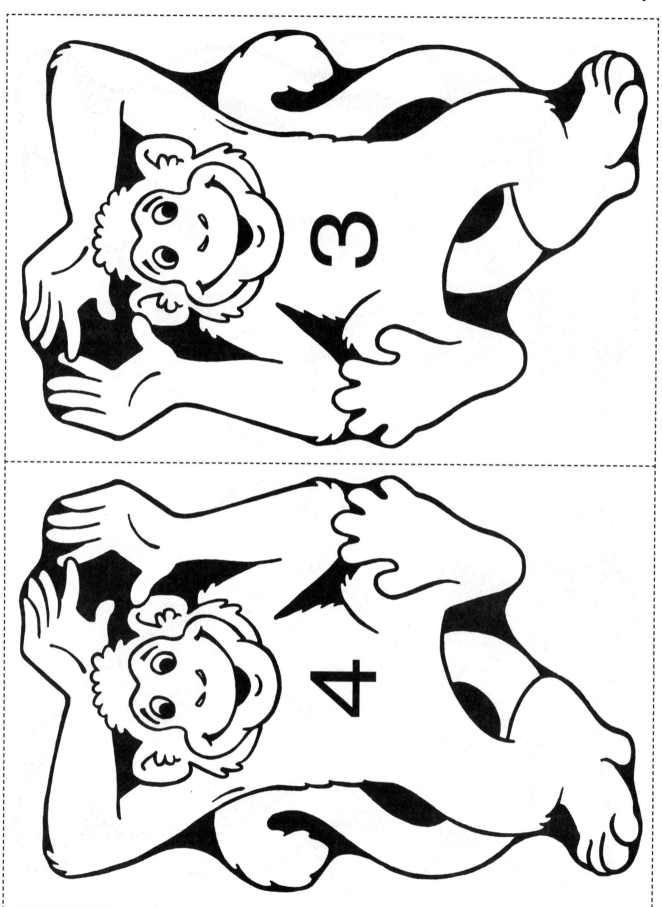

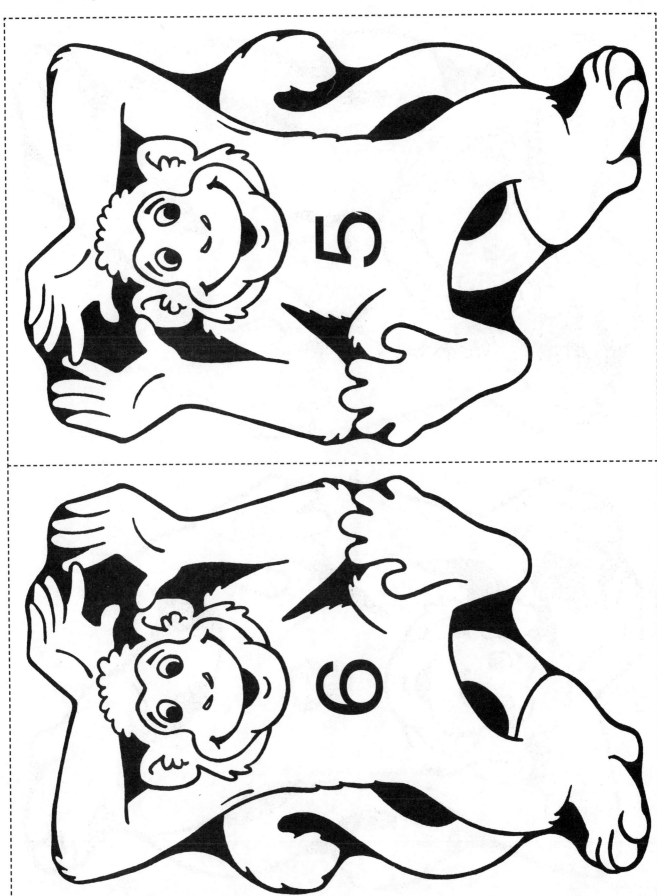

#3529 Math in Action

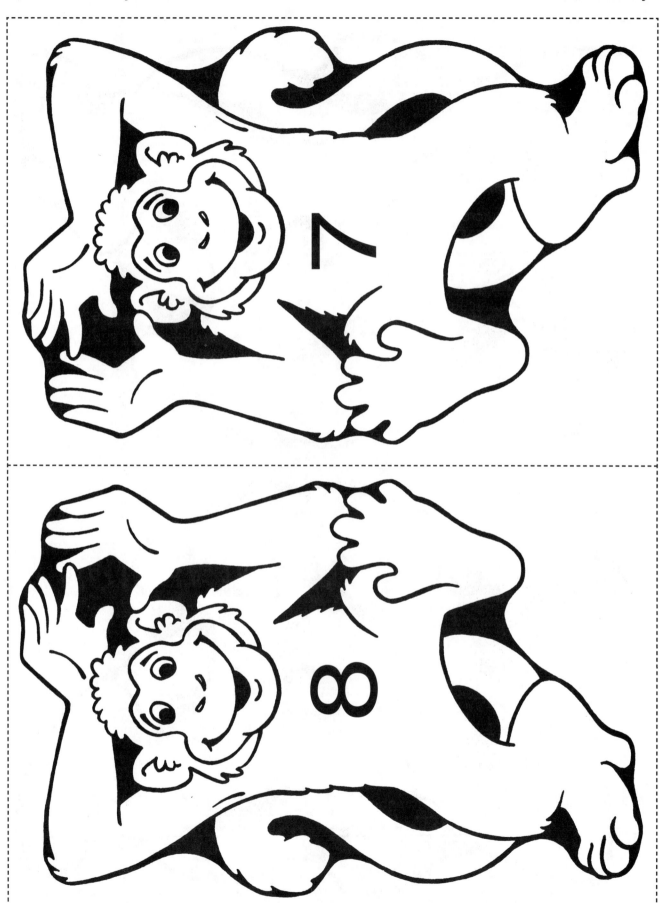

#3529 Math in Action

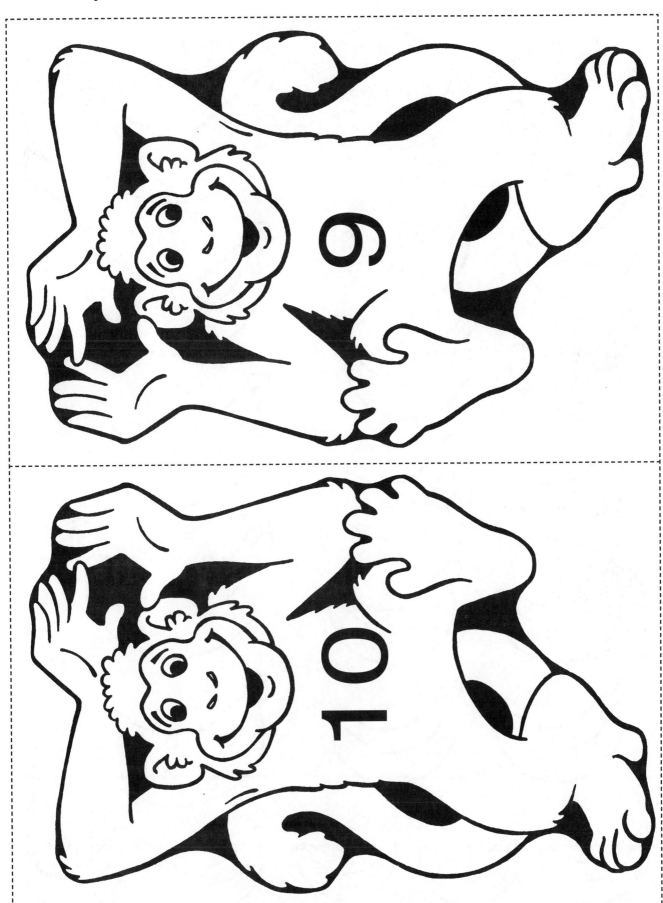

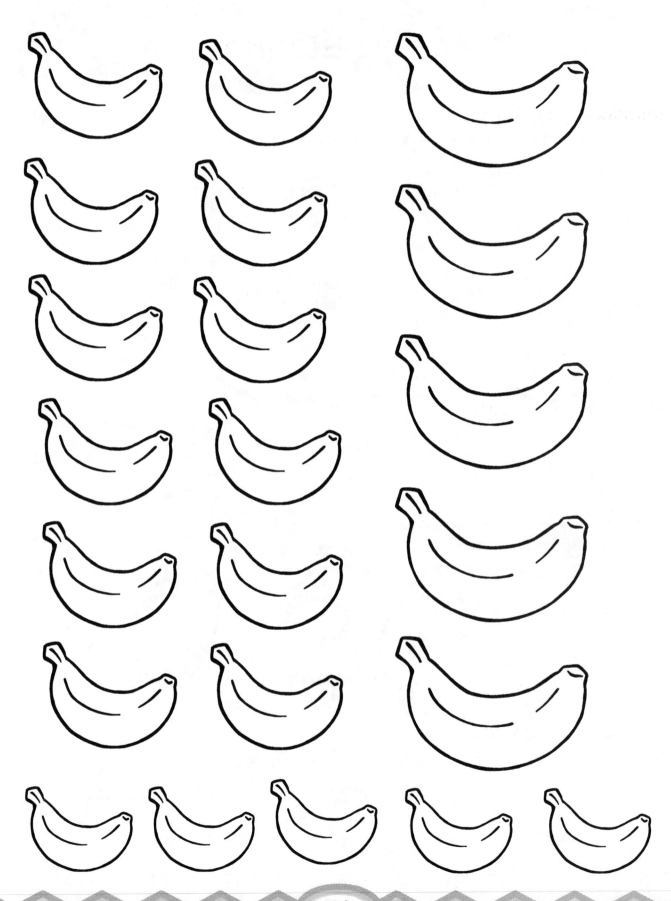

Zebra Stripes

Introducing the Activity

❑ Discuss how zebras have lots of stripes on their bodies.

❑ Have students pretend the stick counters are zebra stripes.

❑ Tell them that the small cards will tell them how many stripes each zebra needs.

Skills

❑ Represents numerals using objects or drawings

❑ Counts collections up to nine

❑ Demonstrates understanding of simple addition

❑ Identifies and continues a given pattern

❑ Creates their own counting pattern

❑ Identifies more or less than a given number

How to Make the Game

❑ Make ten copies of the large zebra (page 18). You may wish to add some decorative grass before laminating.

❑ Make one copy of the small 0–9 zebras (page 19). Color, laminate, and then cut out as small rectangular cards.

❑ Copy, laminate, and cut out the four activity cards (pages 16 and 17).

❑ Place all the materials into a storage container and label clearly. Use the label provided (page 82).

Extra Materials Needed

45–50 plastic stick counters—including plenty of black ones to be stripes for the zebra

Zebra Stripes

✓ Choose one large and one small zebra.

✓ Give your zebra the matching number of stripes.

Colored Stripes

✓ Choose one large and one small zebra.

✓ Use two colors for the stripes (e.g., two red and three yellow stripes for the 5 card).

✓ Count how many stripes in each color.

✓ Record your discovery on paper.

 or
ONE   GROUP

Zebra Stories

✓ Tell your partner a zebra story.

✓ Ask your partner to match the actions with the zebra card and counters.

  e.g., One day the zebra woke up and had four yellow stripes. The next day there was one more stripe. How many stripes did the zebra have altogether?

✓ Find a small zebra card to match your zebra's total number of stripes.

PAIR

Zebra Patterns

✓ Make a pattern with the stripes

  e.g., black, yellow, black, yellow

✓ Ask your partner to say the next few colors and then to continue the pattern.

✓ Exchange roles.

PAIR

17

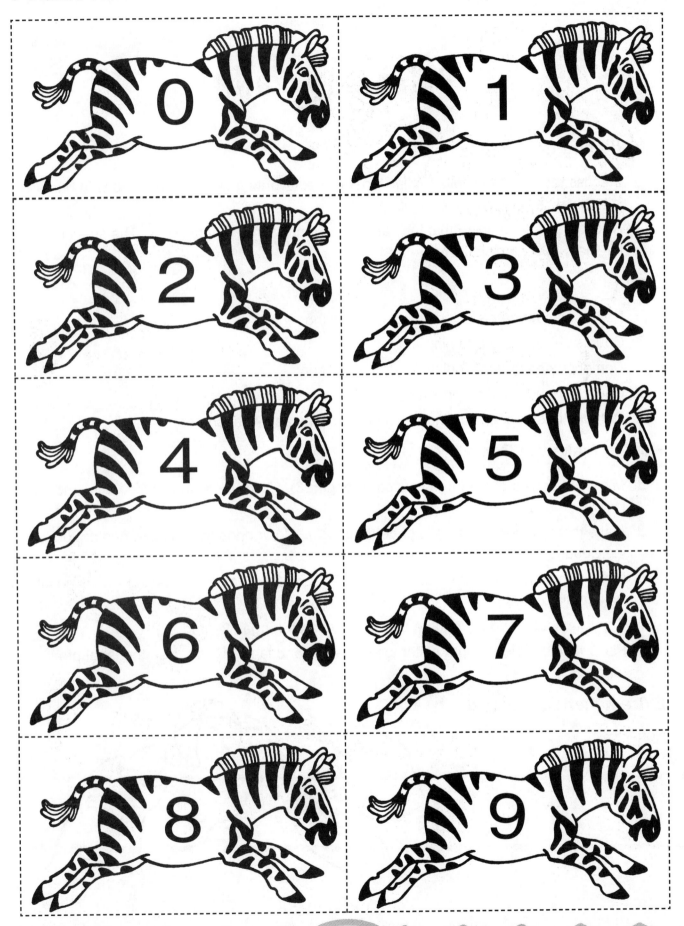

Balancing Balls

Introducing the Activity

❏ Discuss the way seals love to play together. A favorite trick when they are with humans is to balance balls on their noses.

❏ Ask students to imagine that they are playing ball with a friendly seal. The small cards tell them how many balls to use.

Skills

❏ Represents numerals using objects or drawings

❏ Counts collections up to nine

❏ Demonstrates understanding of simple addition

❏ Counts on mentally to add small numbers

❏ Demonstrates understanding of simple fractions as 'equal shares'

How to Make the Game

❏ Make ten copies of the large seal card (page 23). Color these in with crayons, and then laminate.

❏ Make three copies of the balls page (page 25). Color brightly, laminate, and cut out as individual balls.

❏ Make one copy of the small seal cards 0–9 (page 24). Laminate and cut out as small rectangular cards.

❏ Copy, laminate, and cut out the four activity cards (pages 21 and 22).

❏ Place all the materials into a storage container and label clearly. Use the label provided (page 82).

Extra Materials Needed

None

Balancing Balls

✓ Select one small seal card and one large seal card.

✓ Balance the matching number of balls on the seal's nose.

✓ Hide the small card. Ask your partner to guess the number.

 or

PAIR   GROUP

Two Seals

✓ Take a handful of balls and two large seals.

✓ Share the balls between the two seals.

✓ Can the seals share the balls equally? Why?

ONE

#3529 Math in Action

Pattern Balls

✓ Make a pattern with your balls.
   (e.g., red, blue, red, blue)

✓ Ask your partner to continue the pattern.

✓ Exchange roles.

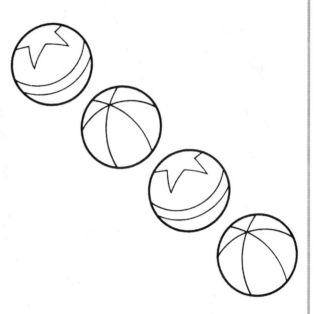

PAIR or
GROUP

Secret Number

✓ Work with a partner.

✓ Put a secret number of balls on your seal's nose.

✓ Show your seals to each other. Do you have the same number?

✓ Do you have more or fewer balls than your partner?

✓ Guess and then check.

PAIR

0    1

2    3

4    5

6    7

8    9

24

Find a Bone

Introducing the Activity

- ❑ Discuss dogs in general and any antics they get up to as pets.
- ❑ Tell students that each dog in this game likes to collect a certain number of bones.

Skills

- ❑ Rote counts forwards to . . .
- ❑ Represents numerals using objects or drawings
- ❑ Counts collections up to ten
- ❑ Represents numbers in symbols and words
- ❑ Places objects into order by size, shape, or number
- ❑ Identifies missing numbers in a given counting pattern
- ❑ Demonstrates understanding of simple fractions as "equal shares"

How to Make the Game

- ❑ Make one copy of each of the dog pages (pages 29–33), so that you have ten dogs in all. Color each dog, laminate, and cut into ten rectangular cards.
- ❑ Make one copy of each dogbone page (pages 34–39)—symbol, numeral, and number words. Color in, laminate, and cut out as individual bones.
- ❑ Copy, laminate, and cut out the four activity cards (pages 27 and 28).
- ❑ Place all the materials into a storage container and label clearly. Use the label provided (page 82).

Extra Materials Needed

None

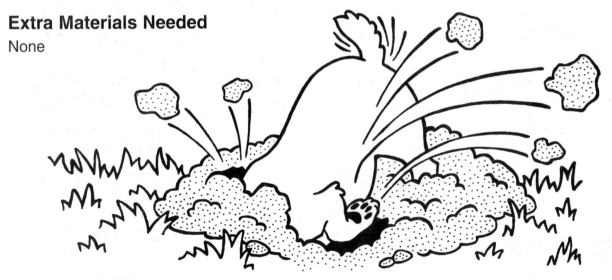

Find Three Bones

✓ Take a large dog card. Find a matching set
   of symbol, numeral, and number word bones.

✓ Compare them with a partner's bones.

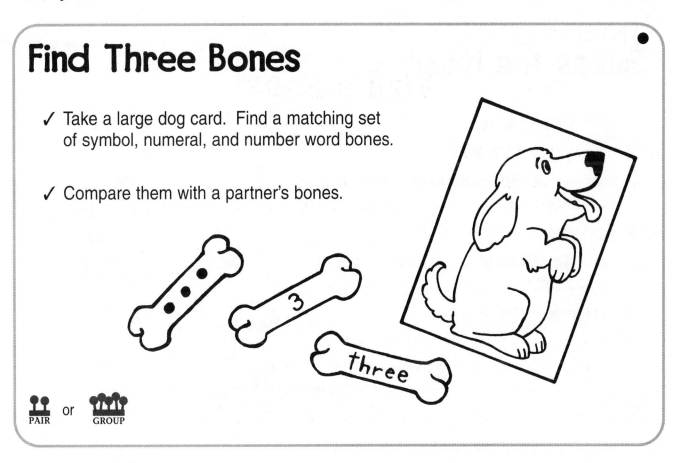

PAIR or GROUP

Sort the Bones

✓ Sort the bones into three piles—symbols,
   numerals, and number words.

✓ Sort each group into counting order.

✓ Can you sort them backward, too?

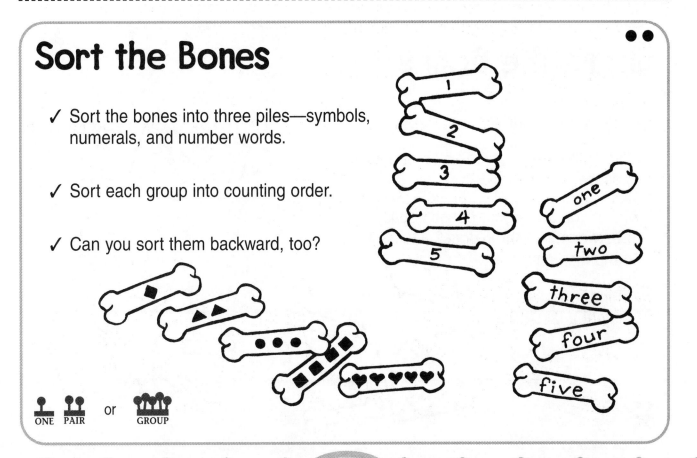

ONE PAIR or GROUP

#3529 Math in Action

Guess the Number

- ✓ Work with a partner.
- ✓ Hold up a symbol bone.
- ✓ Ask your partner to guess how many shapes. Exchange roles.
- ✓ Hold up a numeral bone.
- ✓ Ask your partner to tell you the number that comes before or after.
- ✓ Exchange roles.

PAIR

Share the Bones

- ✓ Work with a partner.
- ✓ Take three dogs each and a handful of bones.
- ✓ Can you share your bones equally between your three dogs? Guess first, and then check.
- ✓ Find two ways to sort the bones so that it is not a fair share.

PAIR

     ©*Teacher Created Resources, Inc.*

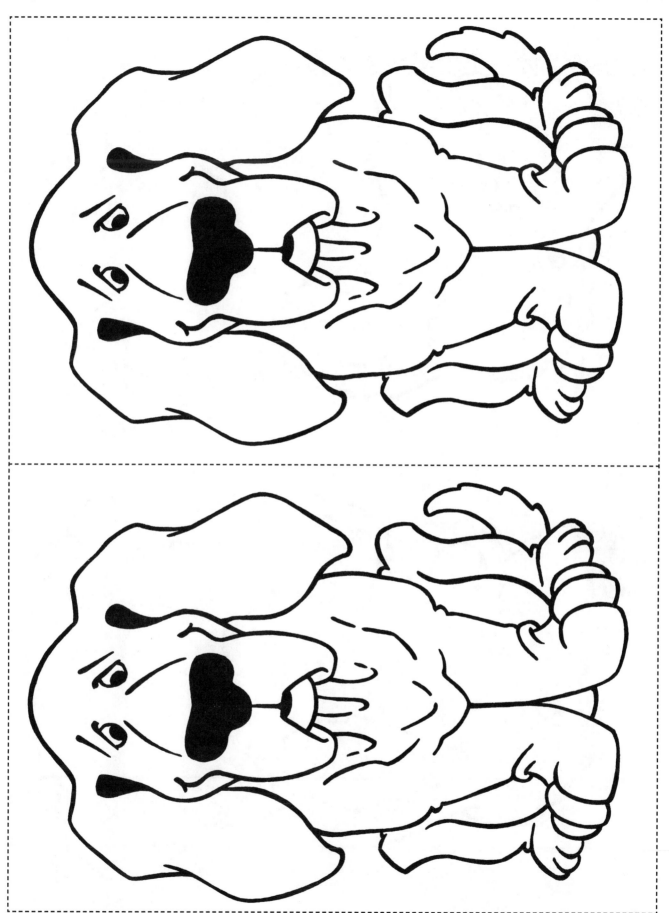

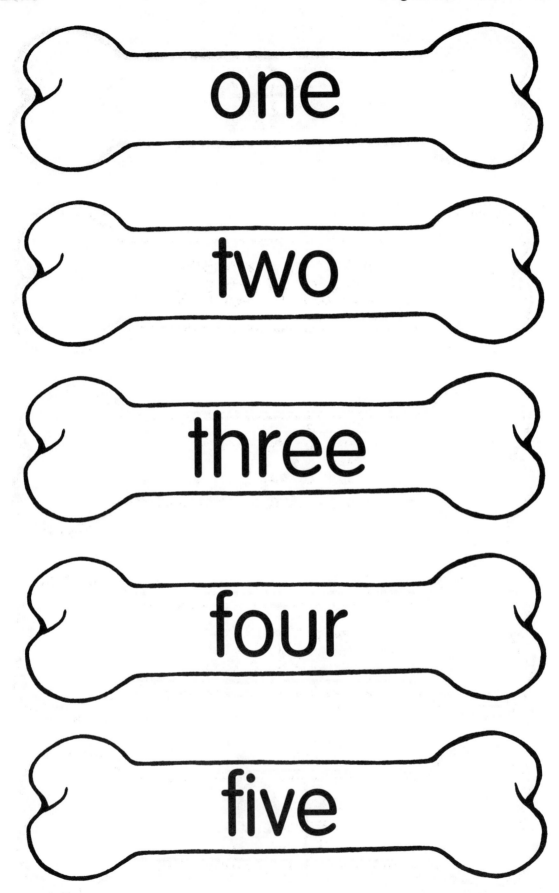

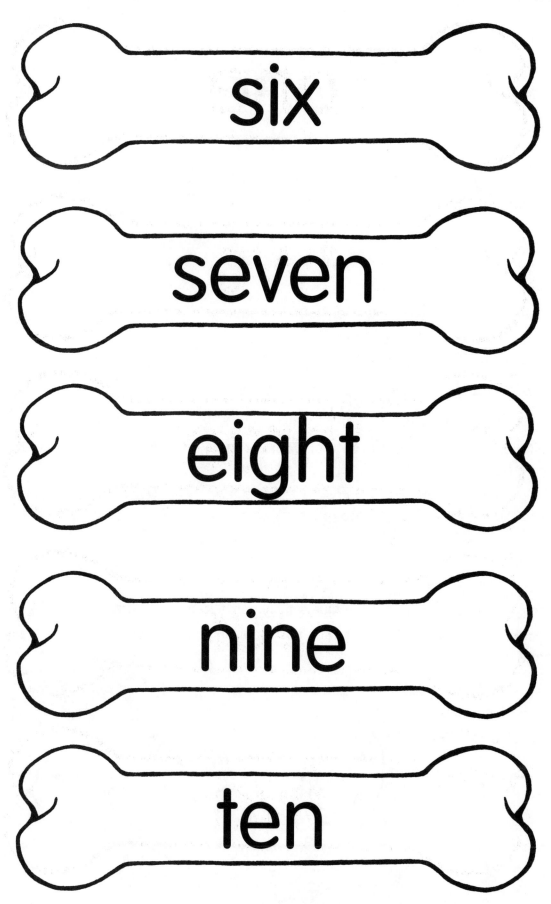

six

seven

eight

nine

ten

#3529 Math in Action

How Hairy?

Introducing the Activity

❑ Discuss how Mr. Hairy is bald. He loves to imagine what it would be like to have hair.

❑ Ask students to pretend each craft stick is a strand of hair on Mr. Hairy's head.

Skills

❑ Represents numerals using objects or drawings

❑ Counts collections up to ten

❑ Places objects into order by size, shape, or number

❑ Invents and records number stories

❑ Demonstrates conservation of number with up to 10 objects

❑ Understands simple subtraction and records results

How to Make the Game

❑ Make ten copies of the large Mr. Hairy card (page 43). Color these in with crayons, then laminate.

❑ Make one copy of the "How Hairy?" 0–9 cards (page 44). Make one copy of the "How Hairy?" number word cards, too (page 45). Laminate and cut out as small rectangular cards.

❑ For extension activities, copy the "How Hairy?" 10–19 cards (page 46). Laminate and cut out. You will need extra craft sticks too.

❑ Copy, laminate, and cut out the four activity cards (pages 41 and 42).

❑ Place all the materials into a storage container and label clearly. Use the label provided (page 82).

Extra Materials Needed

45–50 colored craft sticks

40

How Hairy?

✓ Select one small card and one Mr. Hairy card.

✓ Place the matching number of craft sticks on Mr. Hairy's head.

✓ Find different ways to arrange his hair.

  or

ONE   or   GROUP

The Hairiest

✓ Work with a partner.

✓ Put hair on five Mr. Hairy cards each.

✓ Ask your partner to put them in order from the least to the most hair. Find the small number card to match, too!

PAIR

Hairy Stories

✓ Work with a partner.

✓ Tell each other stories about Mr. Hairy. Model each story with craft sticks.

   e.g., Mr. Hairy has 10 strands of hair. After scratching his head, 3 strands fall out. How many strands are there now?

✓ Record one of your stories on paper.

PAIR

A Handful of Hair

✓ Take a handful of sticks. Guess how many you have. Count them. Place them on a Mr. Hairy card. Find a number word card to match.

✓ Ask your partner to rearrange Mr. Hairy's hair. Guess how many strands now? Count the sticks again. Did moving the sticks change the number? Why?

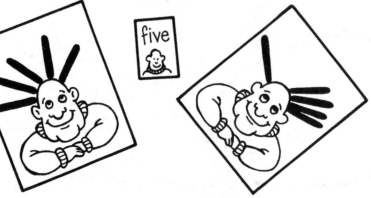

PAIR

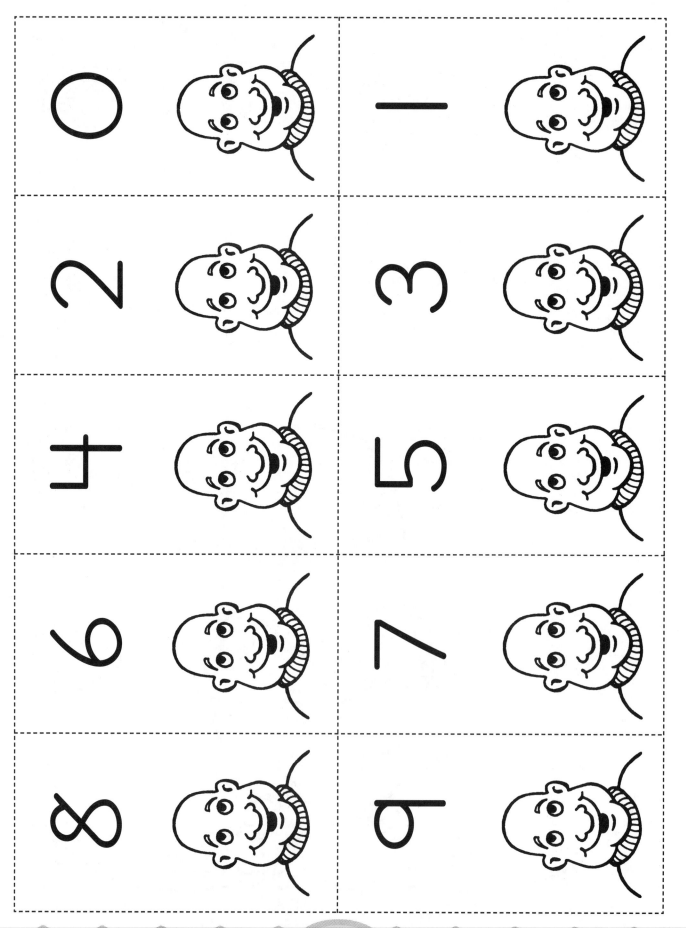

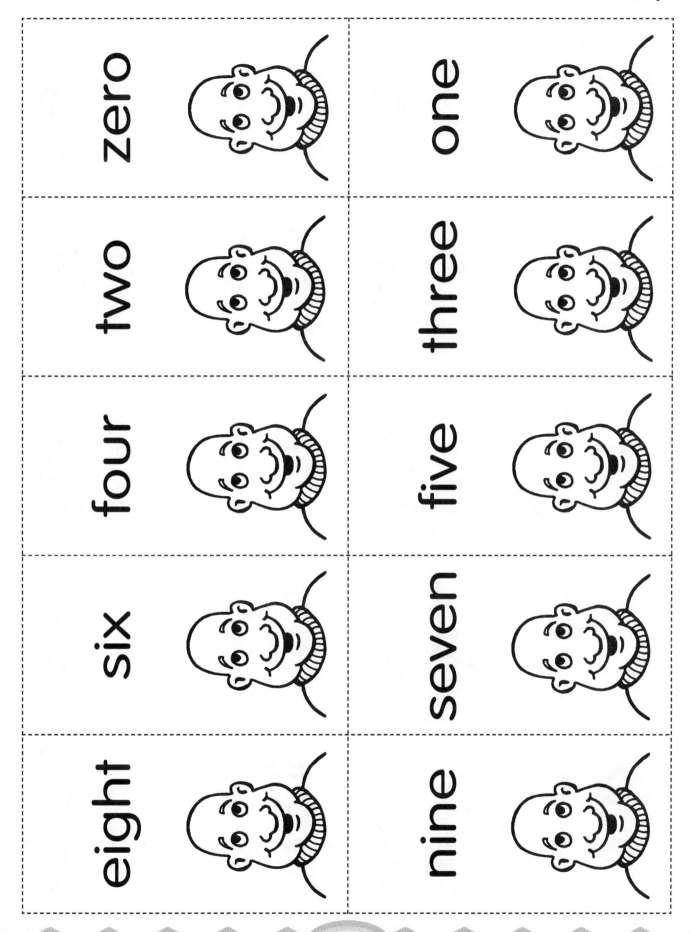

　　　　　　　　　　　　　　#3529 Math in Action

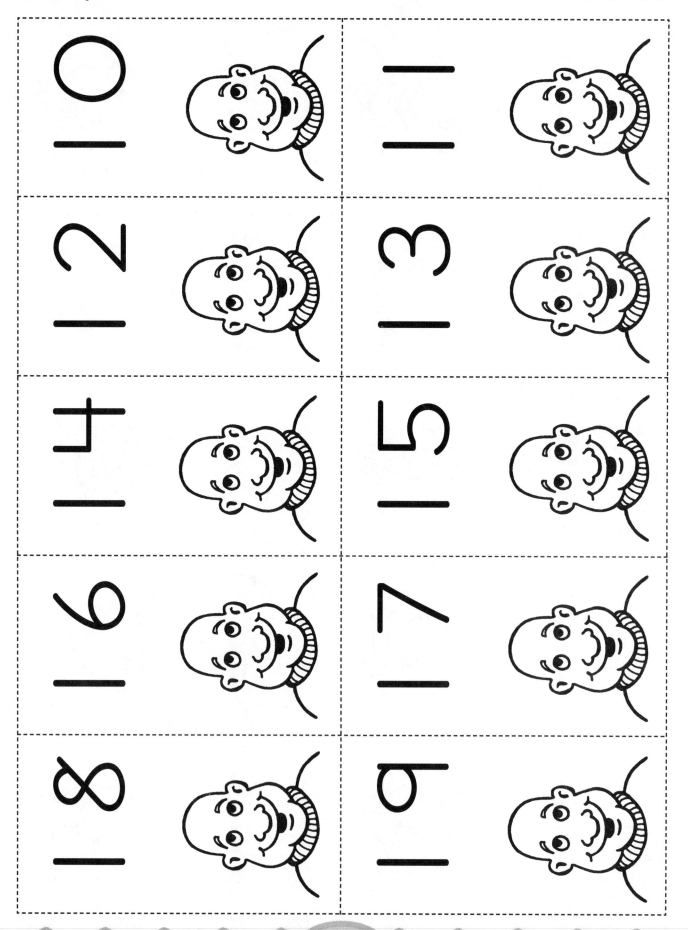

Set the Table

Introducing the Activity

- ❑ Discuss how we set the table with a knife, fork, spoon and plate for each person. Discuss where you put each item.
- ❑ Tell students that the small cards tell them how many doughnuts to put on each plate. They can then find the plastic knife, fork, and spoon to match.

Skills

- ❑ Compares and orders sets of objects using one-to-one correspondence
- ❑ Represents numerals using objects or drawings
- ❑ Counts collections up to ten
- ❑ Represents numbers in symbols and words
- ❑ Identifies a group of objects as odd or even
- ❑ Places objects into order by size, shape, or number
- ❑ Identifies missing numbers in a given counting pattern

How to Make the Game

- ❑ On each plastic fork (see "Extra Materials Needed" below), write a numeral from 0–9. On each knife, write the number words from *zero* to *nine*. On each spoon, draw some symbols in sets from 0 to 9.
- ❑ Make three copies of the doughnuts (page 50) to make 48 doughnuts in all. Color each doughnut, and laminate the pages. Cut out as individual doughnuts.
- ❑ Make one copy of the 0–9 doughnut cards (page 51) and the number word cards (page 52). Laminate and cut into small rectangular cards.
- ❑ For extension activities, copy the 10–19 doughnut cards (page 53). Laminate and cut out. You will need many extra doughnuts.
- ❑ Copy, laminate, and cut out the four activity cards (pages 48 and 49).
- ❑ Place all the materials into a storage container and label clearly. Use the label provided (page 83).

Extra Materials Needed

A colorful set of 10 plastic knives, forks, and spoons, 10 colorful paper plates, a pen/marker that writes on plastic

Set the Table

✓ Select a small card.

✓ Place the matching number of doughnuts onto a plate.

✓ Find the matching knife, fork, and spoon.

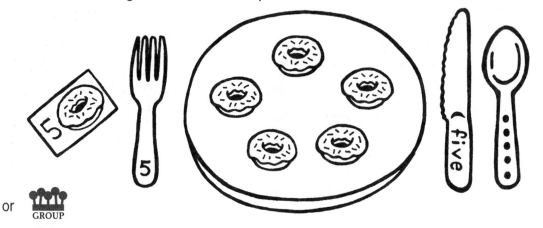

 or

ONE   GROUP

Missing Numbers

✓ Sort all the knives into counting order, then all the forks, and then all the spoons.

✓ Hide some. Ask your partner to tell you the missing numbers.

✓ Exchange roles.

PAIR   or   GROUP

How Many Doughnuts?

- ✓ Work with a partner. Arrange a secret number of doughnuts on your plate.

- ✓ Show them to each other for about two seconds, and then hide them again.

- ✓ Guess whether you both have the same, more, or fewer doughnuts than each other.

- ✓ Check by matching them one to one.

- ✓ Find a small card to match your number of doughnuts.

PAIR

Odd or Even

- ✓ Select a small card.

- ✓ Place the matching number of doughnuts onto a plate. Do you have an odd or even number of doughnuts? How do you know?

ONE or   GROUP

49

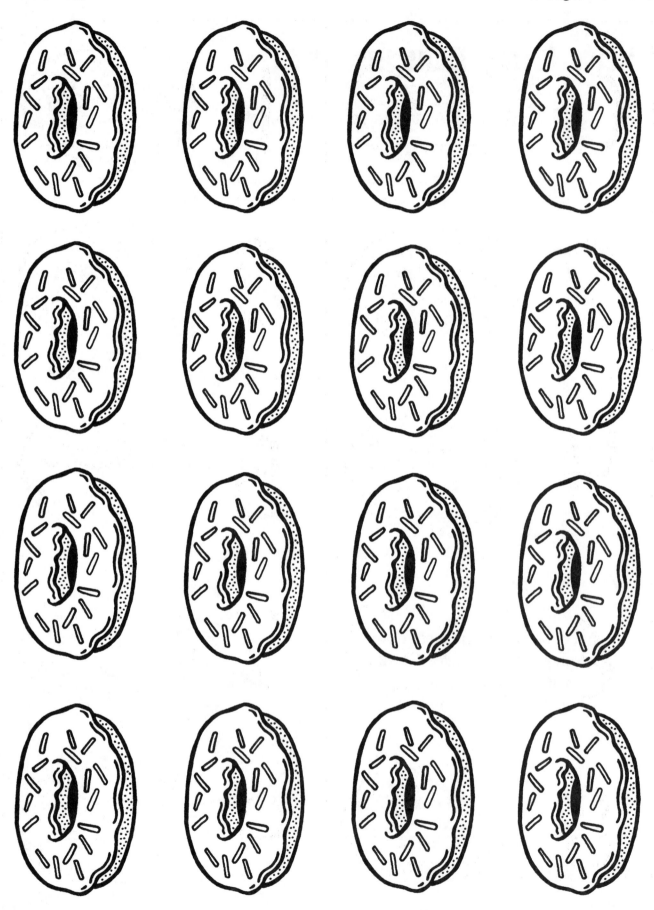

0

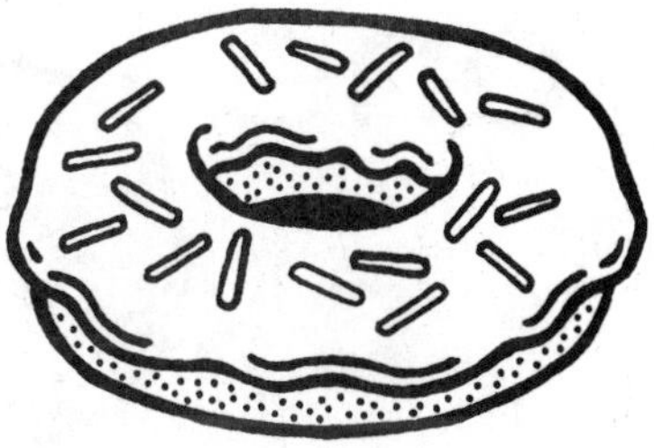

1

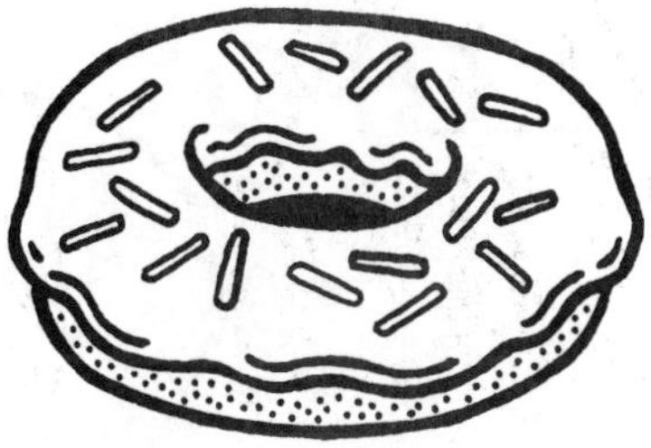

2

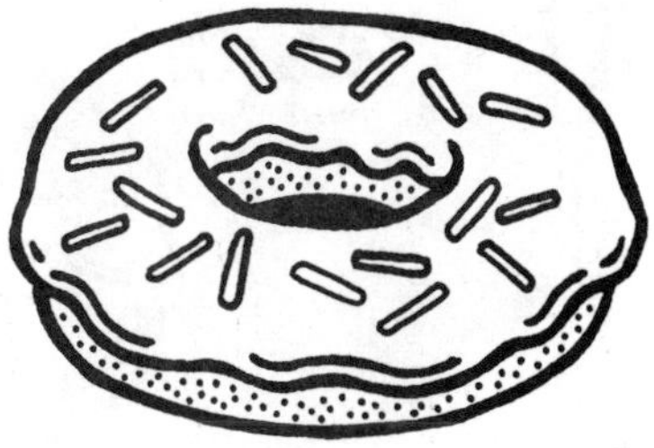

3

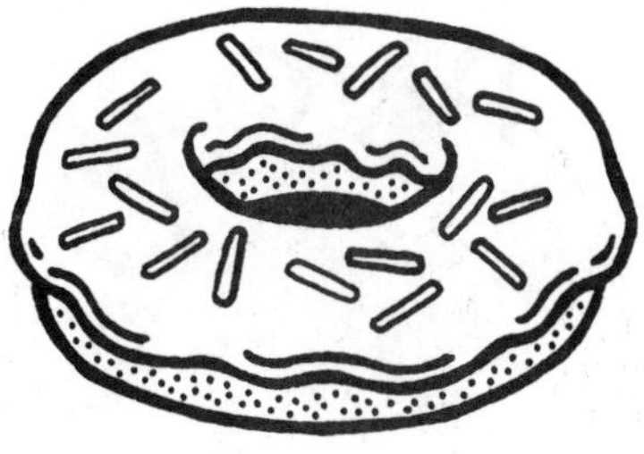

4

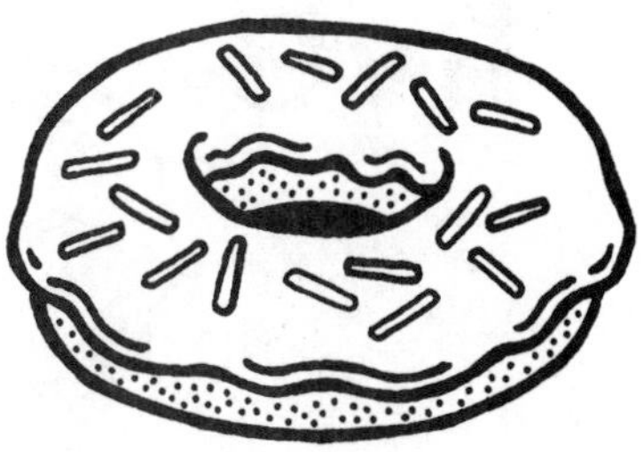

5

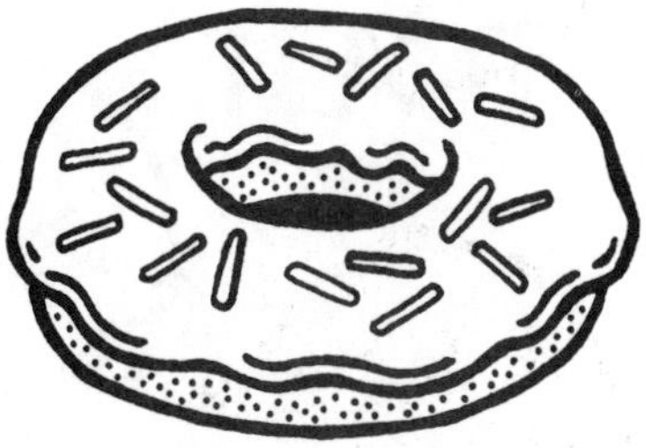

6

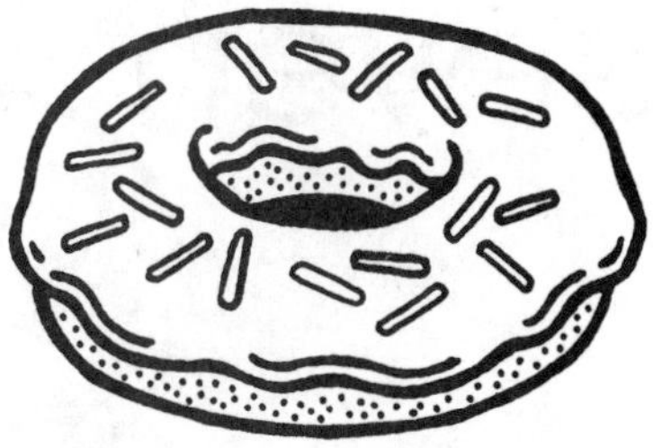

7

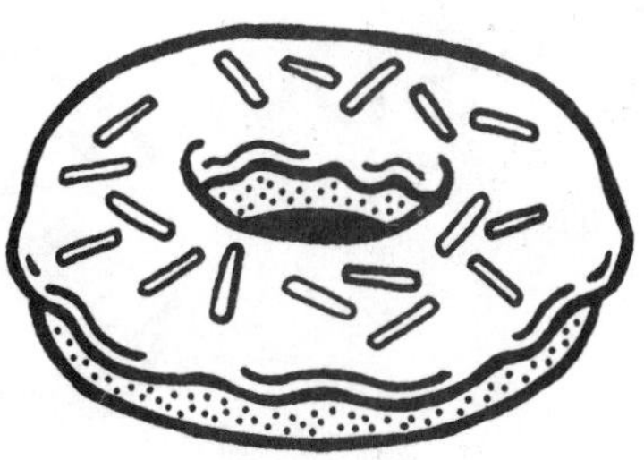

8

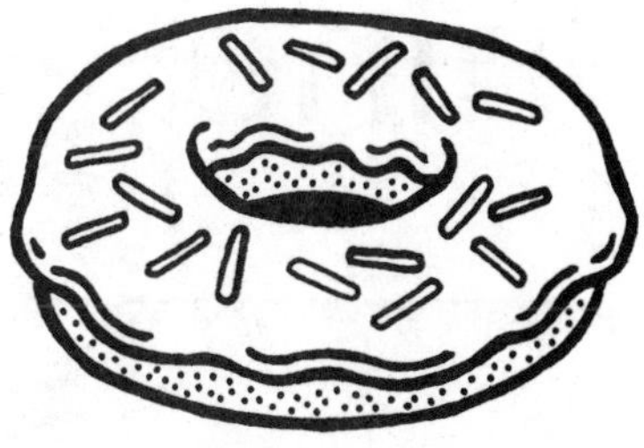

9

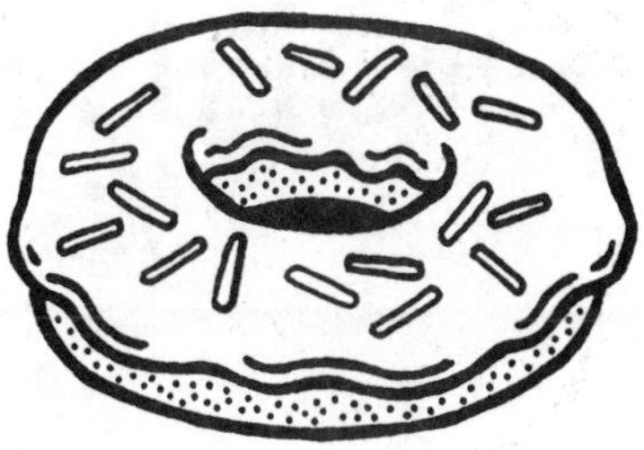

#3529 Math in Action

zero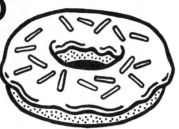

one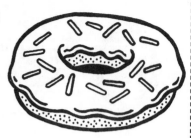

two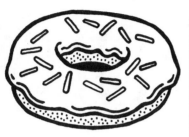

three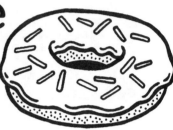

four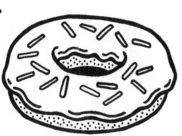

five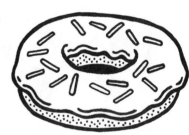

six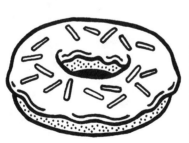

seven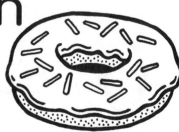

eight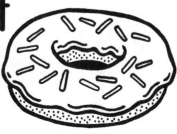

nine

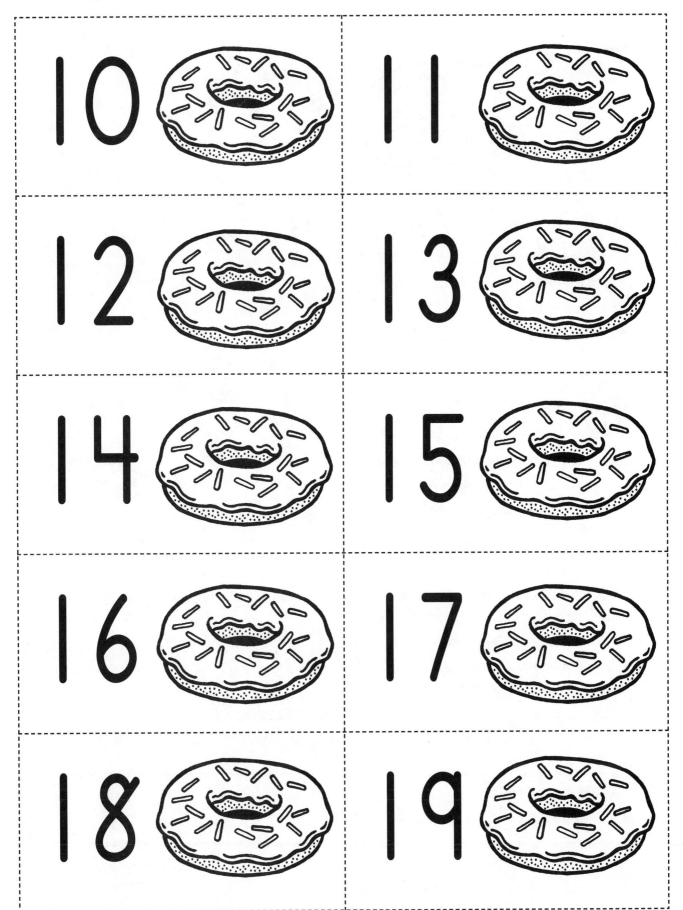

Something Fishy

Introducing the Activity

❏ Ask students to pretend the fish are swimming around in each fishbowl. Tell students that the small cards show them how many fish go in each bowl.

Skills

❏ Sorts and classifies objects into two or more sets

❏ Explains the sorting criterion for a given set

❏ Identifies similarities and differences in objects and sets

❏ Places objects into order by size, shape, or number

❏ Rote counts forwards to . . .

❏ Represents numerals using objects or drawings

❏ Counts collections up to ten

❏ Identifies and continues a given pattern

❏ Records patterns by writing or drawing

❏ Creates their own counting patterns

❏ Demonstrates understanding of simple addition and subtraction

How to Make the Game

❏ Make ten copies of the large fishbowl (page 57). Color each bowl, and then laminate.

❏ Make three copies of the fish (page 58), which will give you 60 fish altogether. Color in, laminate, and cut out as individual fish.

❏ Copy the small 0–9 fishbowls (page 59).

❏ For extension activities, copy the 10–19 fishbowls (page 60) as well. Laminate and cut out. You will also need more fish.

❏ Copy, laminate, and cut out the four activity cards (pages 55 and 56).

❏ Place all the materials into a storage container and label clearly. Use the label provided (page 83).

Extra Materials Needed

0–9 or 10–19 spinner (pages 87 and 88)

How Many Fish?

✓ Take a large fishbowl and a small card.

✓ Put the matching number of fish into your fishbowl.

✓ Turn over another card.

✓ Add or remove some fish to match the new card.

  or **GROUP**

Something Fishy

✓ Work as a team.

✓ Sort the fish into different bowls according to shape.

✓ How many different types of fish are there?

✓ How many fish are in each bowl?

✓ How did you sort the fish?

✓ Is there any other way to sort them?

GROUP

#3529 Math in Action

Fishy Patterns

✓ Work with a partner.

✓ Create a pattern with the fish.

✓ Ask your partner what they think your pattern is.

✓ Exchange roles.

✓ Record one of your patterns on paper.

PAIR

Spin to 20

✓ Play in teams of three.

✓ Use the 0–9 or 10–19 spinner.

✓ Take turns to spin and place the matching number of fish into your team's bowl.

✓ The winning team is the first team to get exactly 20 fish in their bowl.

✓ Try to count on from the number of fish you have at the beginning of each turn.

GROUP

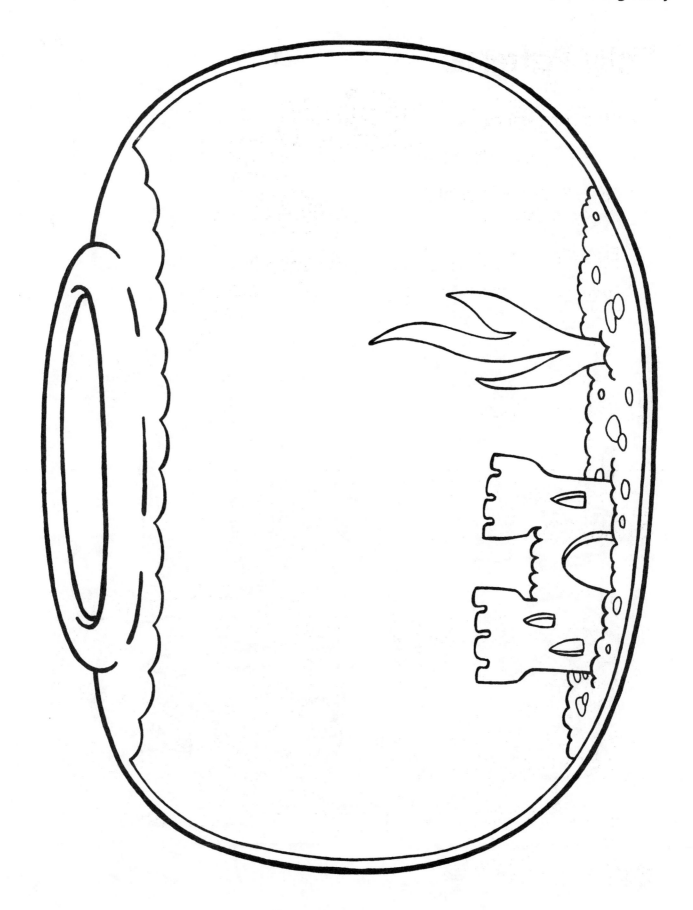

Hopping Frogs

Introducing the Activity

- ❑ Discuss how frogs live in ponds with lilypads. Frogs love to hop from one lilypad to another.
- ❑ Tell the students that the small cards show them how many frogs are on each lilypad at any one time.

Skills

- ❑ Represents numerals using objects or drawings
- ❑ Counts collections up to 20
- ❑ Rote counts forwards to . . .
- ❑ Sorts and classifies objects into two or more sets
- ❑ Explains the sorting criterion for a given set
- ❑ Identifies similarities and differences in objects and sets
- ❑ Places objects into order by size, shape, or number
- ❑ Demonstrates understanding of simple addition
- ❑ Records addition activities in their own way

How to Make the Game

- ❑ If your budget does not stretch to 50–100 plastic frog counters, make four copies of the frogs (page 64), which will give you 60 frogs to start with. Color the frogs, and then laminate and cut out as separate frogs.
- ❑ Make 10 copies of the large lily pad (page 63). Color, laminate, and then cut out each lily pad. Or, using a copy of the lily pad as a pattern, cut out 10 large lily pads from green felt.
- ❑ Make one copy of the 0–9 lily pads (page 65). Laminate and cut into small rectangular cards.
- ❑ For extension activities, copy the 10–19 lily pad cards (page 66). Laminate and cut out. You will need at least another 50 frogs as well.
- ❑ Copy, laminate, and cut out the four activity cards (page 62).
- ❑ Place all the materials into a storage container and label clearly. Use the label provided (page 83).

Extra Materials Needed

50–100 plastic frog counters *(optional)*, one-minute timer, 0–6 die (pages 84 and 85)

Hopping Frogs

✓ Select a small card and place the matching number of frogs onto a large lily pad.

✓ Use a timer and see how many lily pads you can match in one minute.

ONE   or   GROUP   ●

All Sorts of Frogs

✓ Sort the frogs onto different lily pads according to shape. How many different types of frog are there? How many frogs on each lily pad? How did you sort the frogs? Is there any other way to sort them?

PAIR   or   GROUP   ● ●

Collecting Frogs

✓ Use the 0–6 die and three players.

✓ Take turns to throw the die and collect the matching number of frogs on your lily pad. How many frogs did you collect after three turns?

✓ Guess first, and then check. Who has the most? The least?

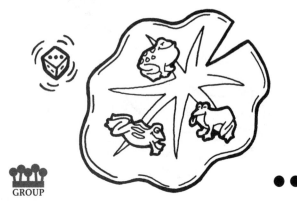

GROUP   ● ●

Secret Frogs

✓ Work with a partner. Arrange a secret number of frogs on your lily pad. Show them to each other for about two seconds then hide them again. Guess whether you both have the same, more, or fewer frogs than each other.

✓ Check, and then repeat. Do your guesses get closer each time?

ONE   or   GROUP   ● ● ●

62

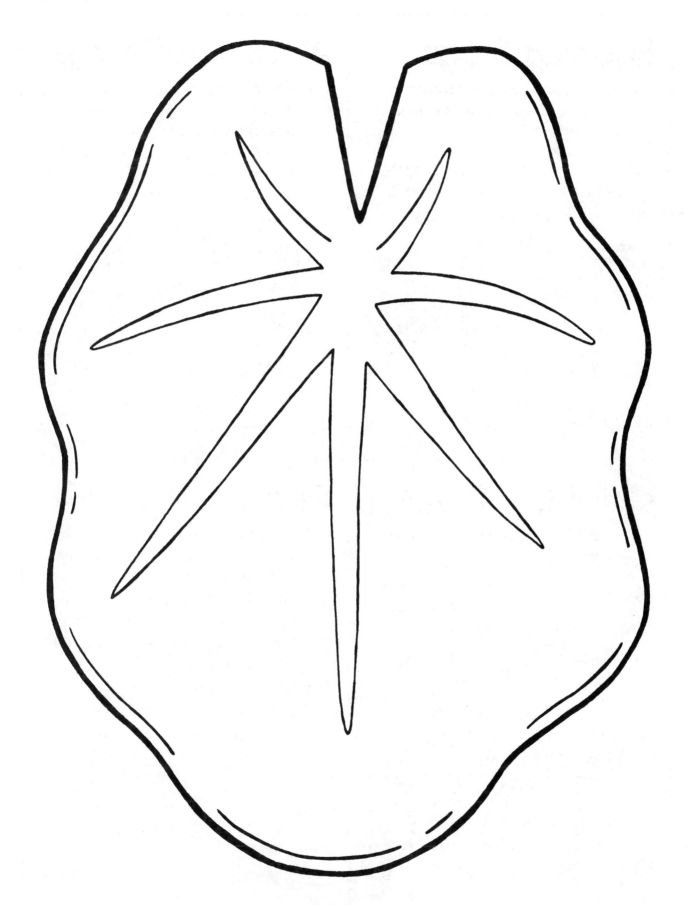

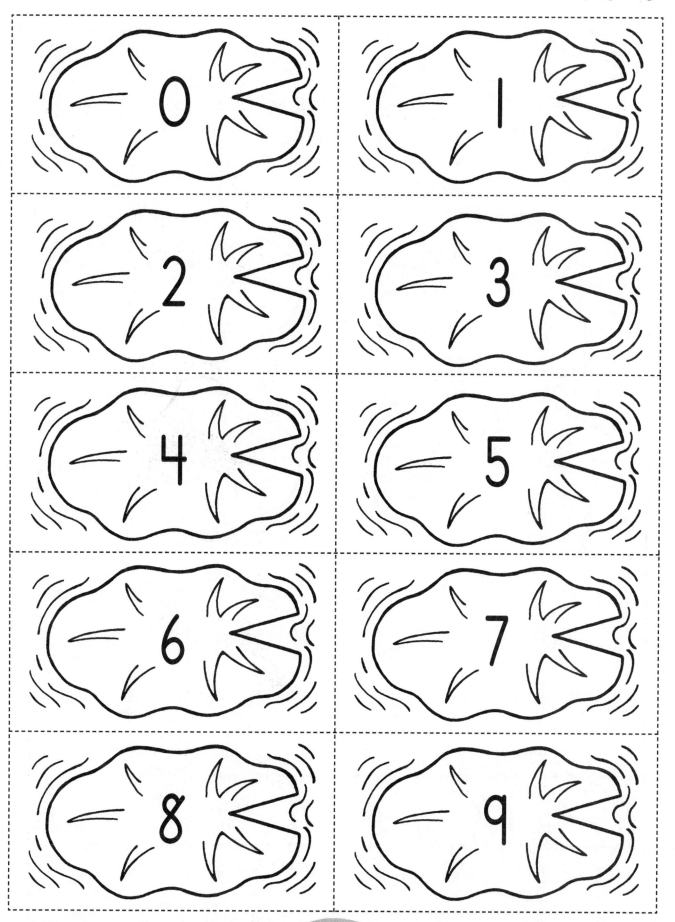

65

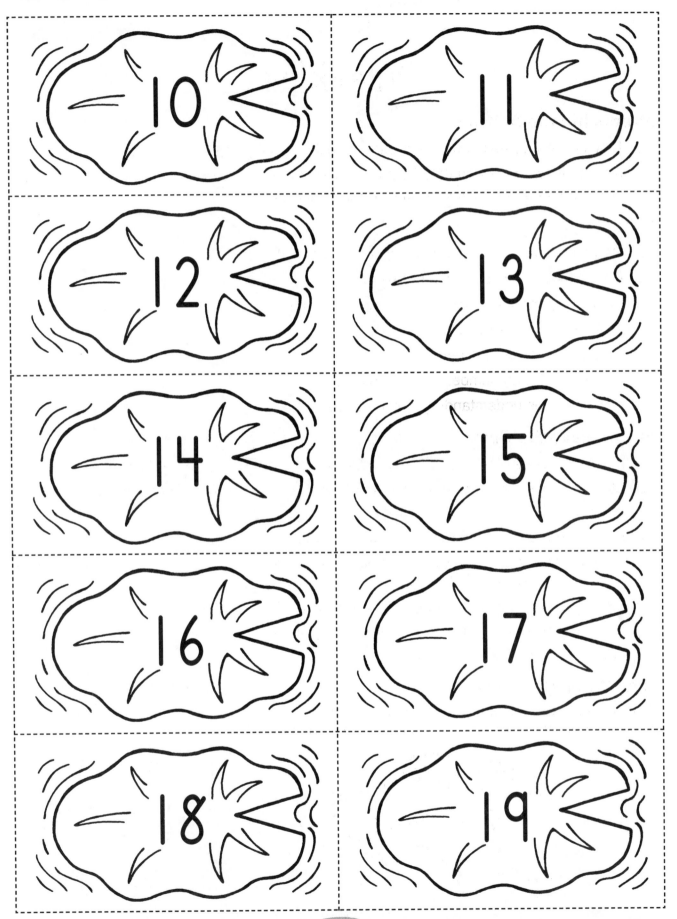

         ©*Teacher Created Resources, Inc.*

Freckles

Introducing the Activity

- ❑ Discuss how some people have a lot of freckles on their face.
- ❑ Ask students to pretend that the counters are freckles. Tell students that the small cards will show them how many freckles to put on each face.

Skills

- ❑ Represents numerals using objects or drawings
- ❑ Counts collections up to ten or twenty
- ❑ Places objects into order by size, shape, or number
- ❑ Rote counts forwards to . . .
- ❑ Rote counts backwards from . . .
- ❑ Identifies missing numbers in a counting pattern
- ❑ Demonstrates understanding of simple subtraction

How to Make the Game

- ❑ Make 10 copies of the large Freckles face card (page 70). Color and laminate.
- ❑ Make one copy of the Freckles 0–9 cards (page 71). Laminate and cut as individual cards.
- ❑ Make one copy of the Freckles number word cards (page 72).
- ❑ For extension activities, copy the 10–19 Freckles cards (page 73) as well. Laminate and cut out. You will need to add plenty more counters.
- ❑ Copy, laminate, and cut out the four activity cards (pages 68 and 69).
- ❑ Place all the equipment into a storage container and label clearly. Use the label provided (page 83).

Extra Materials Needed

50–100 small plastic counters (10 mm diameter) or holes punched from different-colored construction paper

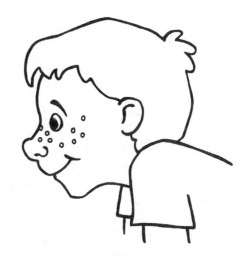

Freckles

✓ Take a large face card and a small face card.

✓ Collect the matching number of counters and place them on your large face card.

✓ Make another face with more freckles.

✓ Make another face with fewer freckles.

✓ Make another face with the same number of freckles.

 or
ONE   GROUP

Missing Freckles

✓ Put the small face cards into counting order forward or backward.

✓ Remove some cards and ask your partner to name the missing numbers.

✓ Exchange roles.

PAIR

Least to Most

✓ Put a different number of freckles on all the faces.

✓ Ask your partner to sort the faces into order from the least freckles to the most freckles.

✓ Place the matching number word card under each face.

PAIR

The Most Freckles

✓ Take two large face cards and a handful of freckles.

✓ Count the freckles and then share them between the faces. Can you share them equally?

✓ Repeat.

PAIR

69

zero

one

two

three

four

five

six

seven

eight

nine

Busy Bees

Introducing the Activity

- ❏ Discuss how bees love to collect nectar from all the flowers in their territory. These bees are busy all day moving in and out of their beehives.
- ❏ Tell students that the small cards show them how many bees are around the hive at any one time.

Skills

- ❏ Compares and orders sets of objects using one-to-one correspondence
- ❏ Represents numerals using objects or drawings
- ❏ Counts collections up to ten or twenty
- ❏ Places objects into order by size, shape, or number
- ❏ Identifies and continues a given pattern
- ❏ Records patterns by writing or drawing
- ❏ Creates their own counting patterns
- ❏ Demonstrates understanding of simple addition and subtraction

How to Make the Game

- ❏ Make 10 copies of the large beehive (page 77). Color each beehive and laminate.
- ❏ Make three copies of the bees (page 78). Color in, laminate, and cut out the individual bees.
- ❏ Make one copy of the 0–9 beehives (page 79) or the number word cards (page 80). Laminate and cut out as individual cards.
- ❏ For extension activities, copy the 10–19 beehive cards (page 81) as well. Laminate and cut out. You will need to add plenty more bees.
- ❏ Copy, laminate, and cut out the eight activity cards on pages 75 and 76.
- ❏ Place all the materials into a storage container and label clearly. Use the label provided (page 83).

Extra Materials Needed

0–6 die (pages 84 and 85)

#3529 Math in Action

Home to the Beehive

✓ Take a large beehive card and a small beehive card.

✓ Collect the matching number of bees and place them on your beehive.

✓ Make up a story to match.

✓ Who has the most bees? Who has the least bees?

GROUP ●

Patterns of Bees

✓ Make a pattern using a handful of bees.

✓ Ask a friend to continue the pattern.

✓ Exchange roles.

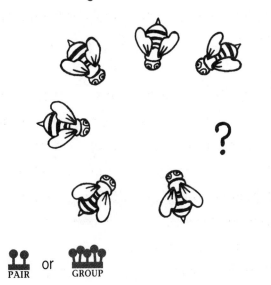

PAIR or **GROUP** ● ●

Busy Bees

✓ Work with a partner.

✓ Give your partner instructions for placing bees on their hive. (e.g., Put 3 bees on the left and two on the right. Make one with two less bees than me.)

✓ Exchange roles.

PAIR ● ●

Two Beehives

✓ Count up all the bees on two hives.

✓ Find a card which shows you how many altogether.

GROUP ● ● ●

75

Match the Number

✓ Place some bees around your large beehive and count them.

✓ Turn over a small beehive card. Add or take away bees to match the new number.

  or ●●●

20 Bees

✓ Each team of four needs a large beehive.

✓ Take turns to throw the die and collect the matching number of bees.

✓ The team wins that collects exactly 20 bees.

 ●●●

Bees Fly Away

✓ Each team of four needs a large beehive and 20 bees. Take turns to throw the die and take away that number of bees. Try to be the first team to have no bees at all.

 ●●●

A Game for Two

✓ Make up your own game for two players.

 ●●●

#3529 Math in Action   ©*Teacher Created Resources, Inc.*

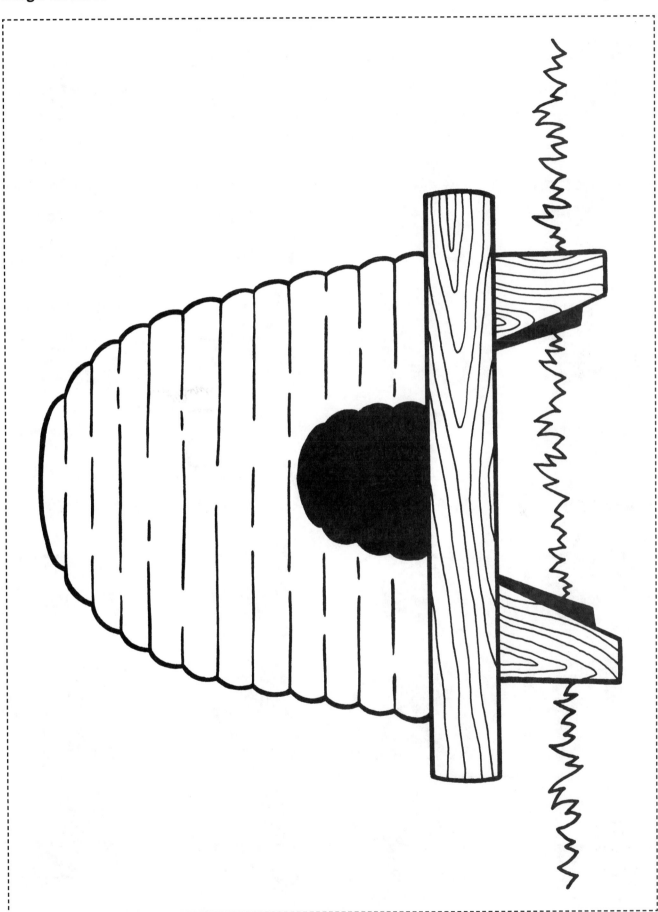

#3529 Math in Action

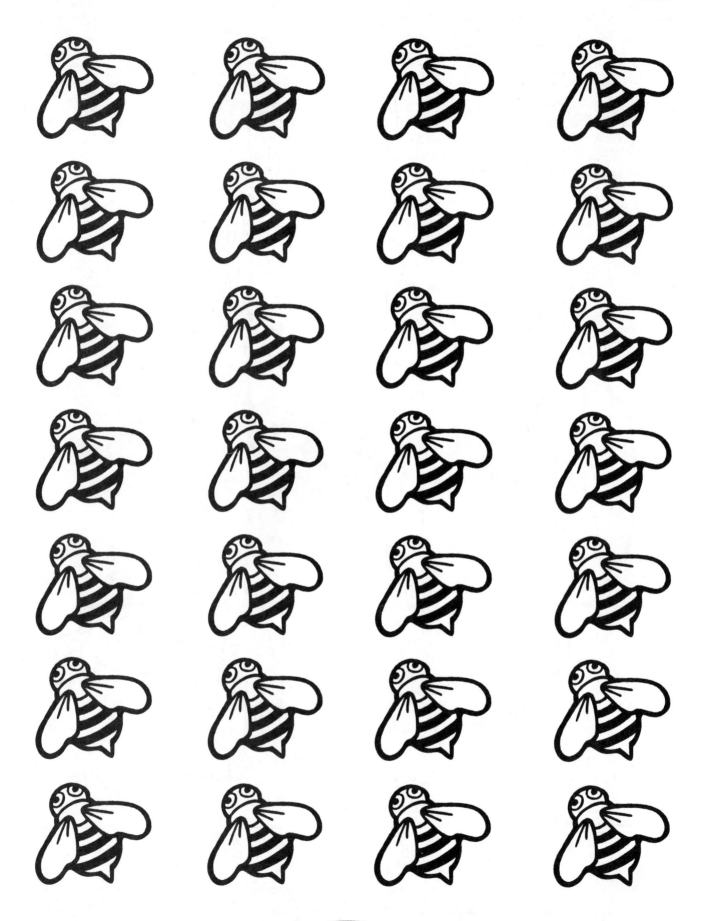

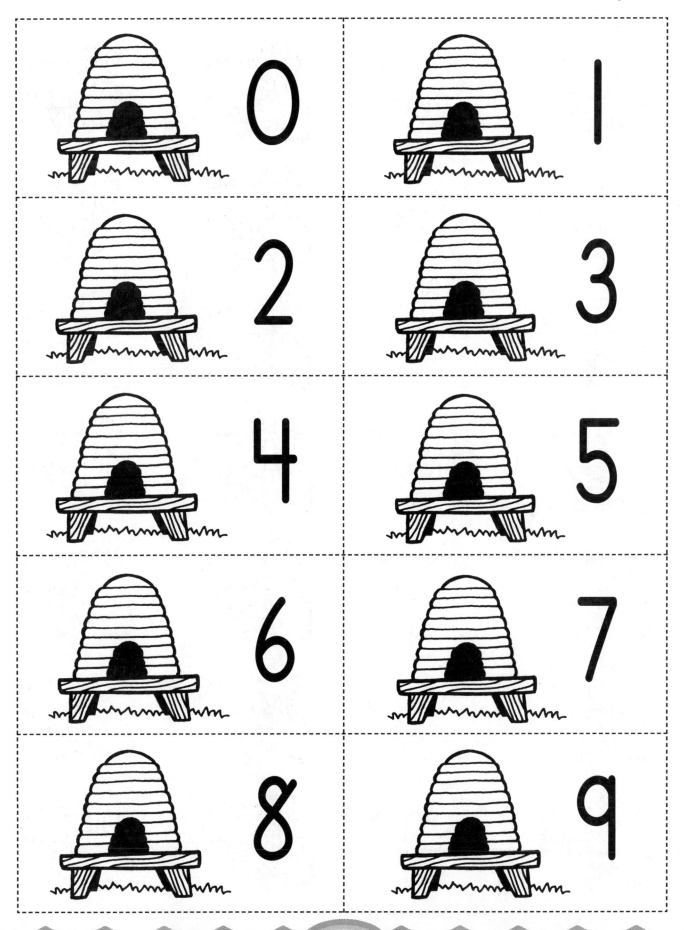

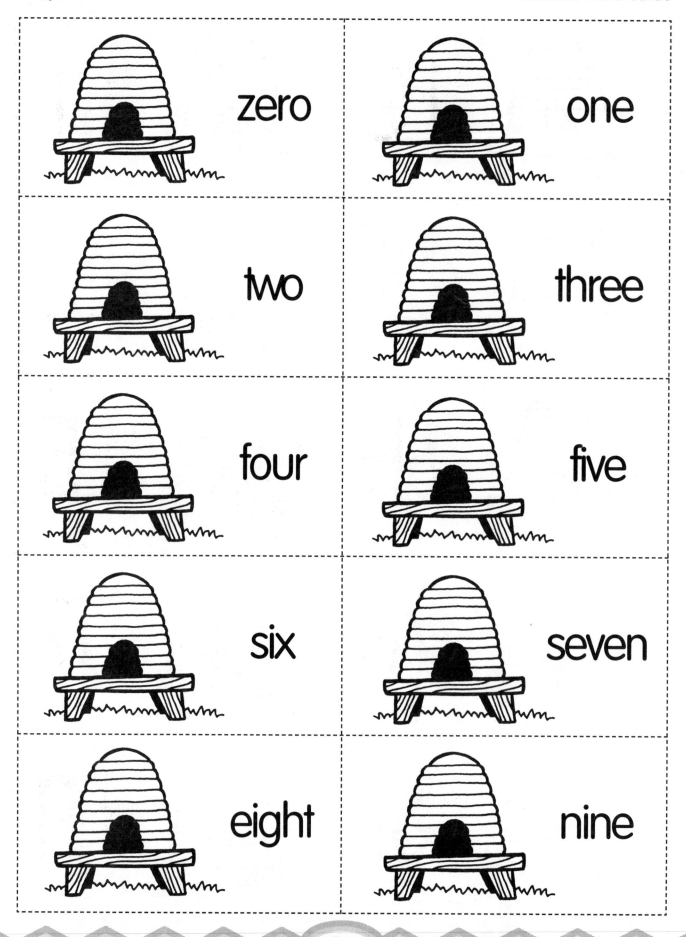

zero

one

two

three

four

five

six

seven

eight

nine

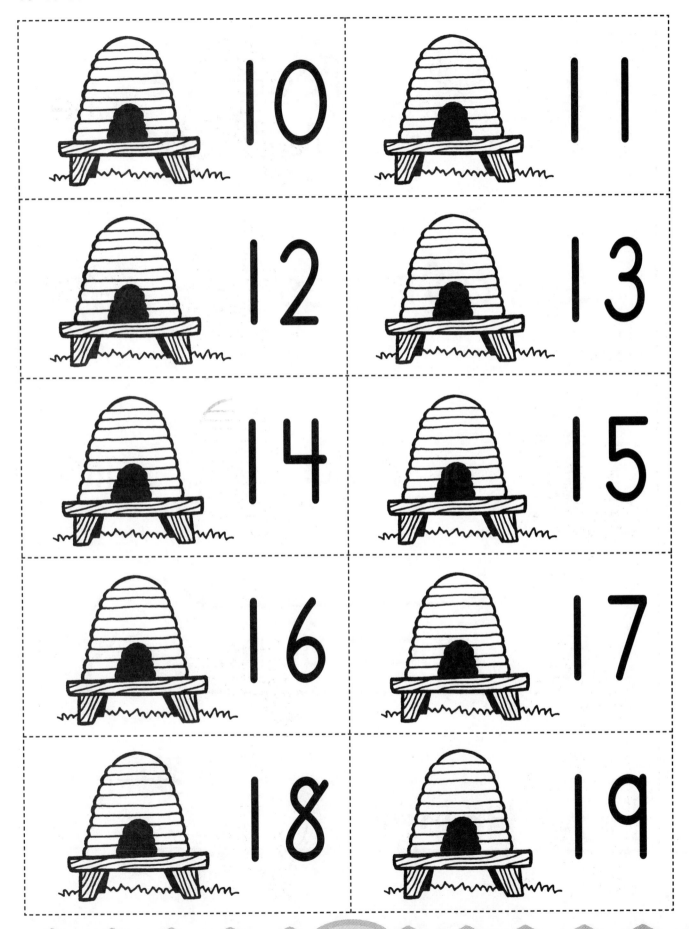

 Feed the Monkeys

Zebra Stripes

 Balancing Balls

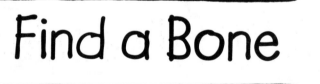 Find a Bone

How Hairy?

Set the Table

 Something Fishy

 Hopping Frogs

 Freckles

 Busy Bees

#3529 Math in Action

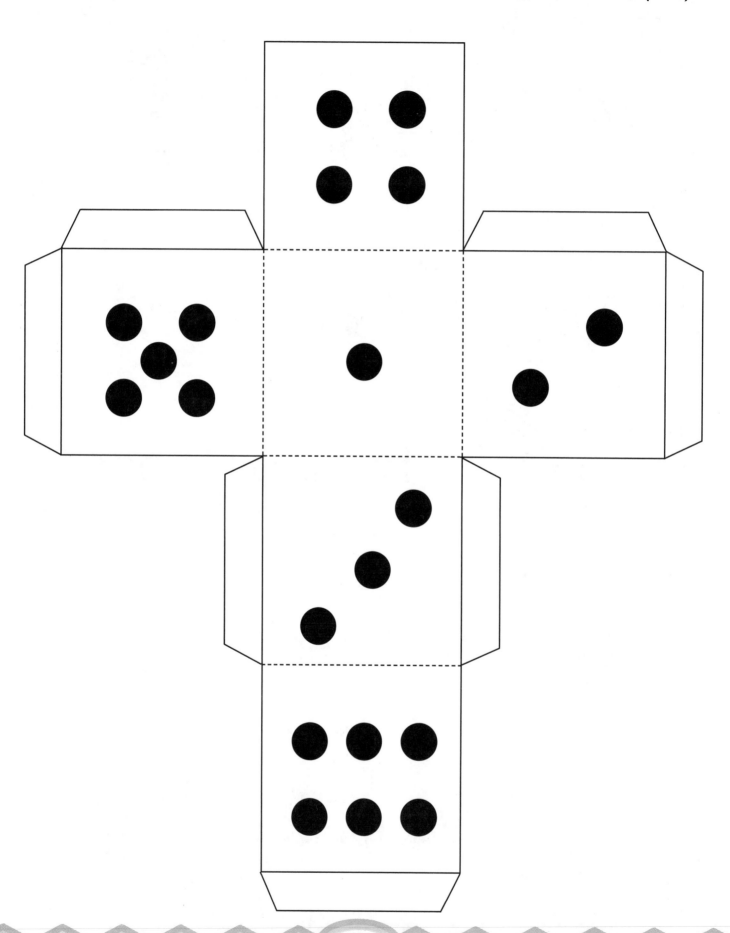

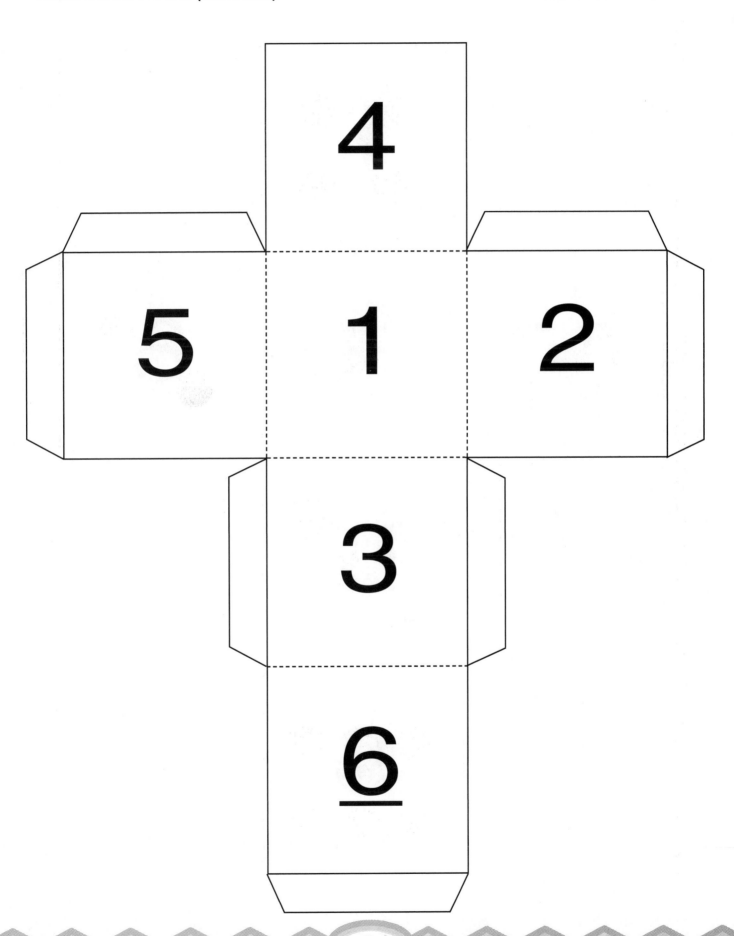

#3529 Math in Action

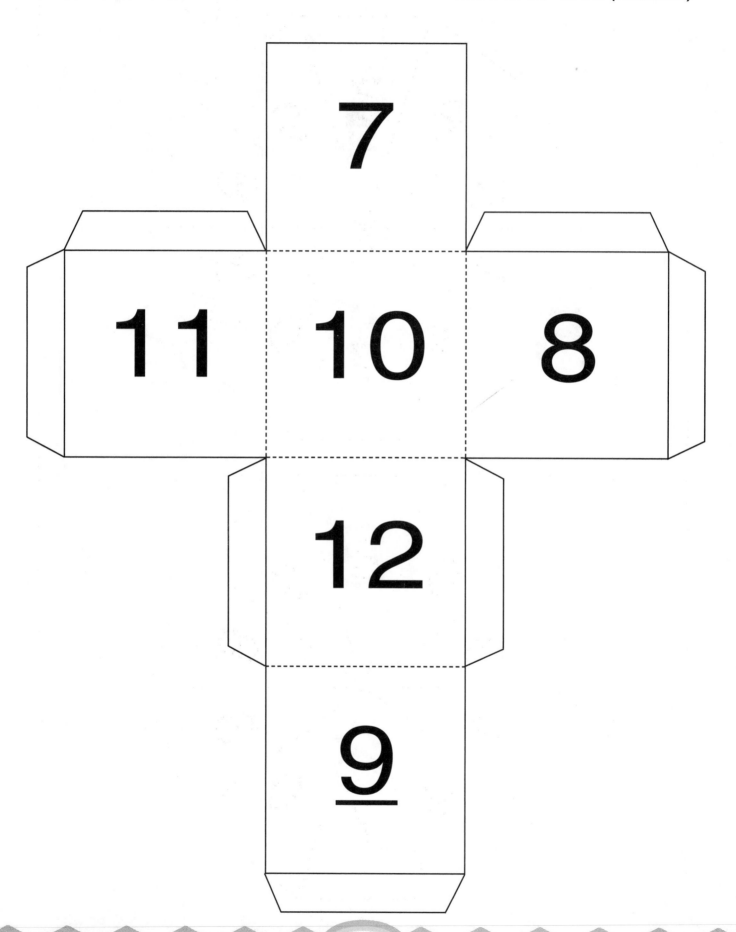

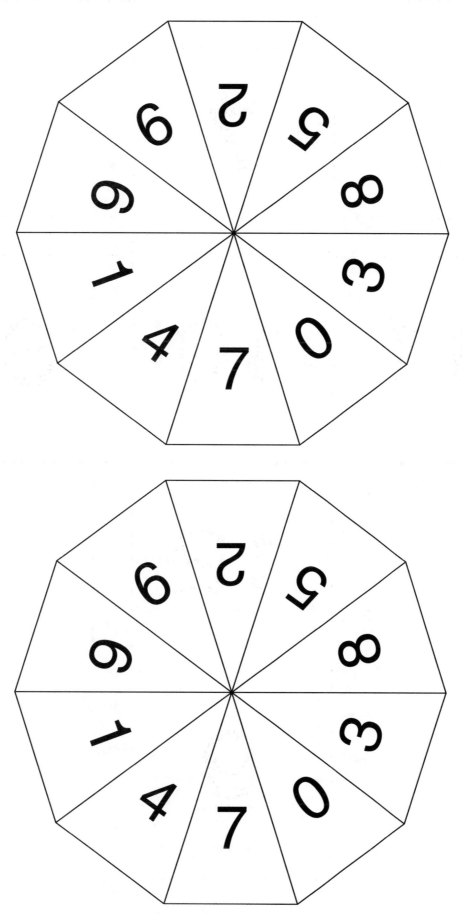

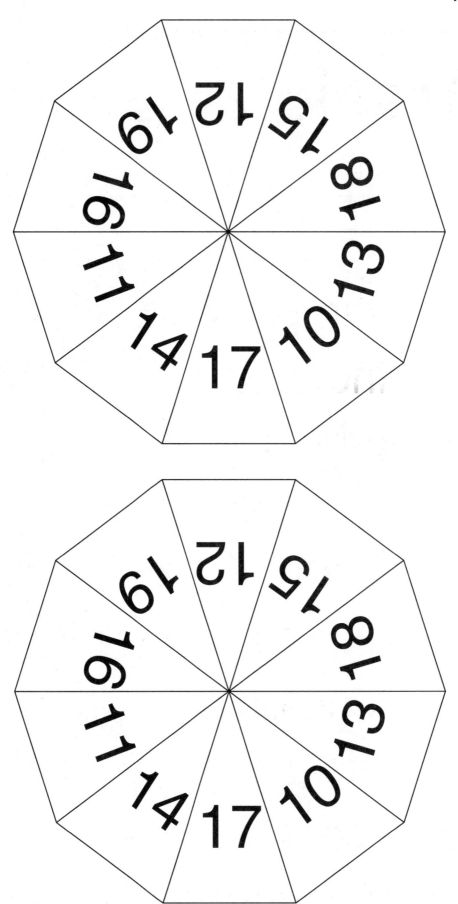

Arabic

0 sifr

1 wahad

2 ithneen

3 thalatha

4 arba'a

5 khamsa

6 sita

7 saba'a

8 thamania

9 tisa'a

10 ashra

  #3529 Math in Action

Chinese

Mandarin

0	ling
1	yi
2	er
3	san
4	si
5	wu
6	liu
7	chi
8	ba
9	jiu
10	shi

WU

Greek

enea

0	miden
1	ena
2	dio
3	tria
4	tessera
5	pente
6	exi
7	efta
8	okto
9	enea
10	deka

#3529 Math in Action

Indonesian

0	nol
1	satu
2	dua
3	tiga
4	empat
5	lima
6	enam
7	tujuh
8	delapan
9	sembilan
10	sepuluh

tiga

#3529 Math in Action

©*Teacher Created Resources, Inc.*

Italian

quattro

0	zero
1	uno
2	due
3	tre
4	quattro
5	cinque
6	sei
7	sette
8	otto
9	nove
10	dieci

#3529 Math in Action

Japanese

0 zero
1 ichi
2 ni
3 san
4 shi
5 go
6 roku
7 nana
8 hachi
9 kyuu
10 juu

ni

©*Teacher Created Resources, Inc.*

Spanish

0   cero

1   uno

2   dos

3   tres

4   cuatro

5   cinco

6   seis

7   siete

8   ocho

9   nueve

10   diez

    #3529 Math in Action

Vietnamese

0   công

1   môt

2   hai

3   ba

4   bôń

5   nâm

6   sâú

7   bây

8   taḿ

9   chiń

10   muôi